Time. Wow.

Cosmic Observations by Neil Clark

For Taylor, my cousin.

Contents

Time.

Wow.

When It's Time to Go

This time, you just wanted a simple life. Go to work. Watch kitten vidcos and food vlogs before bed. Overorder Chinese food at weekends when the hangovers bite.

But wherever you go, there's always something.

Your first ever room had rising damp. The next had moths that ate your clothes.

Your last place had a switch in the cupboard under the kitchen sink, with 'NOT IN USE' written above it in red pen. Your head would constantly be in that cupboard, oblivious to your phone pinging in your pocket with concerned texts from family, stern voicemails from work. You'd stroke the switch for days on end, applying tiny and tinier amounts of pressure. You'd trace the letters with your fingernails and wonder if you'd discovered the reset button for the universe.

When it was time to go from there, you flicked the switch, put the keys on the table and left the flat for the first time since the day you moved in. As your plane took off, you saw an earthquake below, just how you'd imagined.

The new house smelt of fresh carpet and just-dried paint. It felt efficiently put together, like it wasn't passive aggressively wired to the fault lines of the universe.

But you couldn't figure out how to turn the power to the shower on. Your first morning, you had to wash yourself over the sink. It was cold, and the floor got sudsy and wet. Your shivering made you late for your new job.

Then later.

Later still.

Too late.

Absent.

You put a towel over the puddle and spent the next year sat in the bathroom, watching rings of mould circle the loops of fabric, witnessing ecosystems turn from green to light brown, dark brown to black.

You wondered if this was what God was doing. Sitting naked on His bathroom floor instead of turning up to His day job. Shivering. Watching the hues of the globe shift a little each time we loop round the sun.

You found out about your nickname at work. 'Jesus'. You thought it might be because everyone was waiting for you to turn up. That wasn't it. It was because the suit you bought for your first day was getting holier and holier.

You'd never seen a single moth in the flat. You asked the internet if moths can lay eggs underneath human skin. Took the year off to read all 365,000 results.

After you finished reading each article, you inspected your skin so closely, looked so deeply into every pore that every pore became a black hole. Your body became a network of rifts in the space-time continuum, through which the moths were travelling via the ice age and the space age and the stone age, only emerging into the present day to feast on your suit when you were asleep.

Today, you got a letter from the bosses, asking if you owned any other suits. "The holes are getting ridiculous," they said. "They leave you exposed in places that shouldn't be exposed. We see red marks all over your body, like a toddler went mad with a permanent marker."

"We can see right through you," they said.

You knew it was time to go when the earthquake caught up. Shook your flat so hard the towel crinkled on the floor, sent ecosystem crashing into ecosystem. Shook the moths out your pores. Shook open the cupboard doors. Revealed a switch under the bathroom sink that said 'SHOWER'.

You flicked it and left the keys on the table.

Outside, low black clouds touched the tops of derelict

buildings. People ran naked in tight circles, bumping into one another.

As you fled on a stolen scooter, the heavens opened behind you. Flooded the town. Swept your towel into the sea like a magic carpet in the middle of a nervous breakdown.

Your next place will be at the summit of the highest mountain on Earth. The locals will worship the roar and smell of your battered scooter. Feed you. Paint red patterns on your chest and forehead.

You'll be above the clouds, where you can watch the rains wash away the world underneath until you feel your sense of scale floats out of your skull. Until you're standing over a sink, tap running.

You'll see a plane on the horizon, with red writing on the side that says, 'NOT IN USE'. There'll be a glint in the window of the cockpit.

Raise a finger, see if you can beckon it over. The locals will love it if you can.

Different

When you returned to Earth after a decade in space, I took you to our favourite restaurant.

It was the same restaurant as before, except the sign above the door had changed colour and font, and the toilets had new touchless flushes, and the table we always sat at faced another way. All the waiters from before had left and become mortgage advisors and been replaced by the mortgage advisors of tomorrow, and what used to be called a burger was now a locally sourced grass-fed beef patty on a bed of foraged vegetables, served in an artisanal bun.

Over mains, you told me about cells in a human body and how they replenish every seven years. "No fibre of us remains from seven years before," you said.

Over dessert, you told me you were leaving me.

"It's not you," you said as your tentacles played with your food. "It's Earth."

I Fought The Lawn

(And The Lawn Won)

I accidentally drove my lawnmower down a black hole in my garden.

It scrambled time and space, spaghettifying me into a state of perpetual lawn mowing.

That's how I mysteriously disappeared from the face of the Earth, yet my grass remains so immaculately trimmed.

Mirror Tunnel

Somewhere in the universe, someone else is typing these exact words. Such is the vastness of existence.

They're thinking of me, typing these words too.

I'm thinking maybe the universe is an illusion, like a hall of mirrors.

"Interesting thought," we're typing.

Shattered

You came back from space with a box marked 'FRAGILE'.

I was six years old and mischievous. I found it and shook it until the contents turned to powder.

You caught me and told me what was inside: a voodoo replica of the whole entire universe.

Everyone has been living in a meteor storm ever since, and nobody knows why.

It's our little secret.

Unnatural Selecion

As a child, I found a shell on the beach. I held it to my ear and heard the sea gently lapping the shore.

Centuries later, an alien found my skull on a barren Earth. It held it to its antenna and sensed the *bleep* *bleep* *crash* *bang* *wallop* of capitalism and the apocalypse.

Old Light

As flames scorched the Summer air, the barbeque went bad.

We were laughing. We were chatting about holidays. We were saying how nobody cares if the burgers got a bit burnt. It makes the flavour more interesting.

Someone was explaining the maillard effect. Someone else was saying what a beautiful day it was. Clear blue skies.

Your chat always gets all cosmic after a few beers and too much boring conversation around.

You told everyone the sunlight we're feeling on our skin is not the sunlight of now. It's the light of eight minutes and twenty seconds ago. That's how long it's taken for it to travel from the Sun to Earth.

Then I said something. It just came out. Sometimes I get snippy after a few beers and too much of your astrophysics bullshit. I said it also takes less than eight minutes and twenty seconds to fuck up a marriage. Know what I mean?

The silence that followed lasted from Mercury to Venus.

You broke it by asking everyone to please leave. Now, please.

Now you're inside, washing dishes loudly. Now I stand in the garden, old light from eight minutes and twenty seconds ago burning my skin and forming the only shadow left in the garden.

I want to convince the light to turn around. To start its journey again from the beginning, from right before either of us opened our mouths.

Time Lake

We had our first kiss on our minus 100th wedding anniversary. You were a duckling, I was a fish. We dived in for the same crumb at the same time, and our mouths met. At that moment, our future selves were sat in our garden, throwing bread into the pond whilst discussing reincarnation and whether that blemish in the water was in fact a rift in the space-time continuum.

There's No Place Like Home...

Our universe has an extra star that doesn't exist in any other dimension.

We call it the Sun.

I've travelled across space and wormholes my whole life.

When I'm asked where I'm from, I glance at the void in the starry sky, where home should be.

"You wouldn't know it," I say.

Sometimes It Takes 65 Million Years to Find 'The One'

I found everything about you so fucking sexy from the beginning of our date. Your T-Rex watch. Your yellow and green 4x4 vehicle with the film's logo stenciled on the side. Your walking stick, topped with the mosquito encased in the sap.

Before the starters arrived, we were already humming the John Williams theme tune together, getting all kinds of satisfyingly bitchy glares from the other tables.

By the end of the mains (you had the rack of lamb) you'd told me the key points of your life story:

Age ten — going back to the cinema to see the film another twenty times in the opening week;

Age eighteen — going travelling, obtaining DNA from the Jurassic age;

Age twenty-two — getting kicked out of your biomedical engineering degree for conducting a series of morally dubious experiments.

"And what did these experiments entail?" I said.

"So what is it you do?" you replied. "I saw on your profile that you work in the zoo?"

"That's right," I said. "They say I'm a real keeper!"

When you laughed, there was something crocodilian about your grin. A reptilian glint in your eye.

We enjoyed a comfortable few seconds of silence. To me, it felt like a real *moment*. I think you felt the same. You took me by the hand. Your palms were dry and scaly and made me want to buy you some good moisturiser. Your fingernails seemed to be getting sharper and pointier by the millisecond, but I didn't mind.

"Can we skip all this small talk?" you said. "I don't have time for small talk. Maybe not even desert or coffee."

"Shall we go somewhere else?"

"Do you have the keys to your workplace on you?" you said. "The thing is…"

"Oh, here comes 'the thing'," I said. "There's always a 'the thing'. Alright, put me out of my misery. Tell me what 'the thing' is."

"The thing is, I've managed to replicate a lot of the film's science stuff in my home lab, on myself. The biomedical engineering stuff. The DNA stuff, with the fossils and the old mosquitoes. But… I didn't have the time or the money for the other stuff. The infrastructure stuff. The safety stuff. The ethics stuff. You know, the Dickie Attenborough stuff. The cages to keep the dinosaurs away from the general public stuff. The Park stuff."

"Just the Jurassic stuff."

I looked into your eyes. They appeared to be moving round to the side of your face.

Your jaw was starting to jut out. Your teeth were getting longer. It reminded me of my college days on acid and mushrooms, feeling the trip kick in. You made me feel like I was nineteen again.

I could have left you right there, to take care of yourself.

I could have jumped into the nearest vehicle and headed for somewhere safe. Sat with a big bowl of popcorn and watched from afar as everyone in your path got viciously mauled, all silhouettes of half-eaten torsos flying through the city skyline against the backdrop of a full moon.

Maybe I should have paid for my share of the meal and left. Never seen you again. Kept searching online for The One. Plenty more fish in the sea. Genetically stable fish, a few geological periods closer to my own age.

But by that point, it was too late. 65 million years too late.
I was already in love.

Seam

The music video becomes a cultural milestone.

The song is about keeping on dancing no matter what.

The video looks to have been shot in a single, spectacular, sweeping take.

In reality, the video was shot in two takes.

There is a seam.

During the break between shooting take one and take two, a message pings in the band's family group chat: *Sad news. Call home.* They read it separately, in three different dressing rooms. They meet in the middle to make the call. They listen to their mother's voice. They put their hands on each other's backs. For the first time since their journey to stardom began, they feel flesh and blood underneath designer clothes. They hang up and pause, then decide they will finish the day's work. Crazy money had been spent on this production. If major streets can be closed down for this: if traffic can be redirected, tears can be suppressed.

They do the second take. They do it with aplomb. Their private jet takes them home and they get fed like they have hollow legs. In the bedroom they shared as children, they fight over who gets what bed. It's irrelevant. "Aunties and uncles are coming," they get told. "They get the beds. You all get the floor." They get granted compassionate leave. The execs tell them the most important thing is that they're back and ready for the promotional tour. They put on weight for their mother, then lose it for the label. The video gets released. The video goes viral. The video gets talked about by the world. Wannabe editors and directors and film-school lecturers dissect it. They know it was shot in two takes and two takes only. Debate rages in comments sections. Industry boffins speculate on where the seam between the two takes is. If there is a seam, nobody can conclusively find it. They question whether there is one at all. The video's director vows never to reveal this secret, even to the band themselves.

The band members know exactly where it is.

Two minutes in, they are dancing.

They keep dancing.

They don't miss a beat.

Two minutes in, their steps get a lifetime heavier.

A Date with A Time Lord

"You look different from your profile picture," I said. Your face was the same, but your clothes and demeanour were drastically different.

In your profile picture, you were a 1980s throwback and I liked it. Swiped right on it. Thought you looked cool and retro.

"That picture was taken in what you'd call 'the past'" you said. "About thirty-five years what you'd call 'ago'."

"And what would *you* call it?" I said.

"I wouldn't call it anything. It's just me. It's just a picture of me in 1983."

You told me words like 'ago' and 'soon' and 'then' make very little sense to you. You told me concepts like 'late' and 'early' are stupid. To you, getting worked up about punctuality is like an Amazonian frog getting riled about a tiddlywinks competition on Mars.

"Know what I mean?" you said.

"Not really," I said. "Not when I'm too hungry to think straight and we haven't even ordered yet."

"But we *have* ordered," you said. "We've ordered. And we've eaten. And we've fucked. And we've not messaged each other. And we've gone our separate ways. Met other people. You, someone who understands and values punctuality. Me, a fellow Time Lord who knows what I mean. It's all happened. Just not what you'd call 'yet'."

You droned on and on for 'forever'. Told me what I call the 'future' is, to you, like walking around a museum you've visited several times before. You said that sometimes it can be nice to be around someone who's not a Time Lord, because you get to see their reactions to events afresh. But overall, you're bored. Bored of the Time Lord life. You told me a part of you envies me and how I live life the linear way, how I'm so caught up in the 'present'.

When I tried to attract a waiter's attention, you stopped talking and said you were sorry.

"For what?" I said.

"I'm timelordsplaining again. So... what do you do?"

"Don't you already know the answer to that?" I said. "Being an all-seeing Time Lord? And if you already know we're going to fuck and that it'll be nothing more than a one night stand, what's the point in even making an effort?"

You grabbed my hand and looked me in the eye for what a non-Time Lord like me might call 'an eternity'.

"It is what it is," you said.

And that was the moment I'd always remember from our date.

In the end, we ordered and we ate. And we did indeed fuck, and it was what it was. When we went our separate ways, I did meet someone else. I grew old. I died. I went into the ground and became the land. My minerals cultivated other life, which eventually died and cultivated other life again. Earth died, too. But parts of it and remnants of me migrated to other planets, from which new alien species spawned. Before any of that, others died and went into the earth, which produced me.

Theoretically, you were there for it all. You were there when the only remaining remnants of human existence were the plastic bottles and shards of glass we produced. You were there when our towns and cities became fossilised underneath sheets of ice, and you were there when my ancestors were wearing animal hides and painting on cave walls. You always 'were'. You always 'will be'.

But to me, a mere non-Time Lord, that moment you grabbed my hand and you said the fuck we were about to have that you knew was going to happen anyway "is what it is" was the moment you became dead to me.

Skyscraper Head

At school, they call me Skyscraper Head, due to the skyscraper growing on my head.

No doctor will operate on it. They say the plumbing, from top to bottom, is connected to the part of my brain that operates my heartbeat and breathing. One burst pipe and I'm dead, they say. It's a lot of guesswork. There is no precedent. No person has had a skyscraper growing on their head before.

The skyscraper is mainly occupied by office workers. In the evenings, I hear them leaving from the underground carpark that seems to have appeared somewhere deep in my skull. I hear their vehicles whooshing away via the tunnel that drills through the part of my brain that controls my sense of time and space. During the rush hour, those senses get scrambled by all the burning rubber and horns and exhaust fumes.

Know what's cool about having my sense of time scrambled? I get to see the future every evening.

Do you know how tall the building gets in the future?

The building gets three hundred million miles tall.

The building has the universe's highest nightclub, restaurant and aquarium. All the craziest adult shit in existence happens up at the top.

The building has a pad on the roof for space stations from far and wide to dock.

The building is the only skyscraper visible from other galaxies.

Right at the bottom of the building, there's a memorial. They put it there so the universe can always remember where this amazing cosmic skyscraper took root.

The memorial has the date I was born and the date the pipes burst.

At night, when the building is empty and the streets and roads and tunnels are silent, everyone I ever knew gathers at the memorial to remember me; the schoolkid they called Skyscraper Head.

Drifters

I volunteered at peak apocalypse.

When you watch your pension go to shit, then your job prospects fizzle to nothing, then you don't know if you're going to eat again, then you literally don't know if the sun is going to rise the next day, you get to the point where you just think 'fuck it'.

A few days later, the forms are signed and you're getting launched into deep space with a hundred thousand others in the same boat.

We all watched Earth from the spacecraft's viewing deck. We watched it stretch the limits of our sight as we drifted further out.

It was a curved surface of toxic clouds, frozen seas and derelict land.

It was a scarred sphere getting smaller and smaller.

It was a microscopic speck, dwarfed by the other dying planets.

"I still see it," I said to the people round me – strangers, yet suddenly brothers and sisters in arms.

"I still see it too," they said.

"Now I don't."

"I still do."

"Now I don't either."

Then the alarm went off. It was time to begin our cryo-sleep.

• • •

Waking up in space after a thousand-year sleep feels like jolting upright from a dream in which you're constantly falling. Except, the sensation of constantly falling doesn't ease as you realise it was just a dream and now you're awake.

The sensation of waking up and looking at the clock and realising you've slept in. That's another thing that took hold. Except this time, you haven't slept in by an hour or two. It's been a millennium. And it's not like the consequence is getting a little telling off from the boss, or getting mocked by your colleagues for being late. No, the boss is dead. Your colleagues are dead. Your friends. Your family. All of them, hundreds of years dead.

We gathered together, us strangers in arms, and made

awkward quips about having slept like a log. After breakfast, we caught up on the news from the time we'd lost to hibernation.

The last transmission from Earth was nine hundred and eighty-four years ago. They told us that humankind was doomed. They thanked us for our service. They told us we should fend for ourselves out here. Not to worry about reporting back, because there would be nothing to report back to. By the time we watch this, they said, the only life left on the planet will be the bacteria that can survive near geothermal springs.

So there it was. We were the drifting log from the tree that fell in the forest when nobody was around to hear it fall.

We gathered on the viewing deck and we looked out to the stars.

We knew its light would have faded too much to be visible from where we were. Still, a group of us tried to pinpoint where the Sun would be.

And we could have sworn we saw it winking back at us, like the ghost of a loved one in an unfamiliar crowd.

Swipe Night

Midnight & Noon were a match on each other's Tinder.

One messaged the other as the other was going to sleep.

The other replied as they got up.

The world got in the way of them ever meeting.

Midnight gazed and lusted at Noon's light reflecting off the moon, forever pining for what might have been.

Sleeping with The Fishes

A black hole opened in my ceiling and swallowed my bed.

My landlord refused to replace it, claiming I was liable.

When I moved out, I hid a fish in the black hole.

The stink it made transcended space and time, ruining his property portfolio forever.

Our Rhythm

When you fell to Earth, you promised to teach me how to navigate the universe. In return, I said I'd show you how to dance.

Together, we spent the rest of time waltzing through the cosmos —

1-2-3-moon,

      1-2-3-star,

            1-2-3-moon,

[Unfinished]

Every morning, I'd ask this barista how he was, and he'd always say the same thing — "I'm here."

Then one day, he wasn't.

That was years ago. But I still think about that guy, all the time.

Apple Juice

As a kid, he'd drink apple juice on the rocks out of a tumbler to be more like his dad.

As an adult, he drinks apple juice out of a tumbler to be less like his dad.

The More The World Got Damaged

(The More You Cried)

You collected your tears. First in a jar. Then a bucket. Then a pool. A lake. An ocean.

Soon, you flooded the whole world in salt water.

Earth became a giant teardrop, streaming down the cheek of a sobbing universe.

Glue

At the Chinese takeaway, I order my food and I get it handed to me in a steaming hot paper bag. In the time between ordering and receiving my food, I have these conversations with the lady who runs the place.

We talk about next to nothing. We talk about the weather. We talk about funny or annoying habits her other customers have. We talk about stuff to do with my work. We talk about China. We talk about the days we've had, how things change with the time of year because of the climate or holidays or whatever. One time, when no other customers were around, she gave me a tutorial on how to chop a carrot so the pieces look like little goldfish. Our conversations are a million tiny dots, but over the years, they've become a huge canvas you take a step back and see something whole and beautiful.

One time I told her how my boss was a massive dick, and how everyone was quitting because of it. She told me about her chefs. How they'd been there for decades. How staff stay with you if you treat them right, which saves you so many headaches in the long run. She told me that's why the food here is so good.

I go there whenever I have a bad hangover or I've had a shit day at work. Something about their wonton soup glues me right back together.

This time, I was both things. Hungover and just had a shit day at work. I'd made a mistake. A customer called me a fucking cretin. Said I couldn't organise a piss up in a brewery. Said he was going to take this right to the top so the people who were paying my wages would know all about it and would replace me with someone who wasn't some bleary-eyed waster. He stormed off, only to storm back and grab my ID from around my neck to get my full name.

Sometimes I go into the takeaway and she's busy or not there for whatever reason.

This time, one of the chefs came out from the kitchen to take my order. I'd never seen him, but I felt like I knew him. I felt like his hands had pieced me together a million times. I told him so.

Then I took my steaming hot bag of food home and I ate, and I felt this cruel and shattering world become something whole and beautiful again.

Relaunch

One day you woke up and told us you'd just returned from space, and that Earth was a globe-sized allergen that was suppressing your ability to think straight.

You said the stars were your epinephrine injectors.

You said you were a prisoner to gravity.

So we got you a trampoline and put it in the garden.

You slept through the day, then we'd hear you on it all night.

You told us you were going to keep improving on it. Keep upping those seconds in the air to minutes.

Then hours…

…Days

…Years

…Eternity

What We Can Learn
from The Death of Mr McKenna

They found my old high school history teacher, Mr McKenna, dead behind a bookcase in his home. Neighbours had complained about the smell.

I looked into his cause of death. Apparently if you drop something behind a bookcase or a wardrobe, you should never lean into the small gap between it and the wall to retrieve it. If you lose your balance, you might get stuck. If nobody finds you, you might die. Apparently, this is very much a thing.

Instead, move the bookcase or wardrobe first. It might be a bit of a pain, but then again, so is slowly dying alone.

I don't remember many lessons from school. Only those from Mr McKenna's.

I remember him spending a whole afternoon convincing us 'however' and 'therefore' are two of the most powerful words in the English language, and we should always consider using them in any conclusion to any essay. I remember someone asking him what the point in learning history was. He told us, amongst many other things, history presents us with an opportunity to learn from our mistakes of the past.

It must have been awful for Mr McKenna. All alone, lodged against a wall as his last breaths left his body. The bookcase that killed him must have been stacked with so much amazing literature. Books about wars, scandals, revolutions, migrations, all kinds of hardship.

In all those pages, I bet there was nothing warning about the potential perils of getting stuck behind a bookcase. Maybe if there was, he'd still be alive today.

These words are going to be in a book. These very words, right here.

Maybe this book won't stop any wars. However, maybe it will end up on someone else's bookcase. Maybe when that person gets old and they live alone, they won't die stuck behind it as a result. Therefore, these words about Mr McKenna's death would have saved someone's life.

I think Mr McKenna would have liked that.

Italy

I went to Italy alone this time. When I returned, you asked me why I hadn't taken a single photo.

I told you the older I get, the more I enjoy the ephemeral nature of memories.

"The memories would still be ephemeral if you took a photo or two," you said. "It'd also mean you could share them."

"Share them with who?" I said.

I turned to look at you.

You weren't there.

Hadn't been for years.

Star

I befriended a sad, dying star.

By the end, I had to hold it to keep it warm.

"Hey," I said. "Light years away, someone is gazing at the night sky, seeing you in your pomp. A radiant, fiery ball of energy..."

It sobbed a neutron sob.

Then I felt it go cold in my arms.

Scars Are Decorations

For forty-three years, I globetrotted with that leather suitcase.

When everyone bought the one with the wheels and the retractable handle, I kept carrying my life around in that bulky old thing. When both my arms got too dead to lift it any further, I'd drag it along, sweeping all kinds of dust bunnies and gunk off airport floors, train station steps, puddled potholed streets.

When rips appeared, or when the handle got worn-in, I sat in my hostel or motel room and put plasters on my fingers, then I'd patch the case up, sewing a miniature flag of whatever country we were in on top of the holes.

I don't remember who, but someone somewhere once told me scars are decorations.

Then in Riga, I pulled it off the baggage carousel and it just collapsed, like some frail old dude having a cardiac arrest. Spilt its guts out everywhere. Shed half its flags. Caused a bit of a scene, people rushing down to their knees to help out. In the end, I had to scoop everything up and fireman's lift it out of there. I've taken painkillers for my back ever since.

Whatever home means, I took it back there. Home. I opened it up and sat it empty on my front doorstep. Filled it with compost and turned it into a flower bed. Closest thing I ever had to a garden.

I have the suitcase with the wheels and the retractable handle now. It's spared me a few dead arms and gunk bunnies, I'll give it that.

And when I'm back here, back at whatever home means, I sit out on my doorstep at night. Sip a beer. Tend to the flowers. Chat to them about the past, like some old dude talking to some dead dude.

The Boy in The Jacket

I found a note in the inside pocket of this amazing jacket I just bought from a vintage clothes shop. The paper was a pinch away from crumbling between my fingers, but I could still make out the phone number written on it. Underneath were the words—

'Call me'.

I called. I told you how I got your number.

You remembered the jacket. "That jacket is over fifty years old," you said. "I wrote that note forty-eight years ago. Forty-eight years and seven months. And two weeks this Saturday."

You told me what it was like to dance with the boy who wore it. "We were like a pair of figure skaters who already knew our gold medal was in the bag." You said that sometimes, you still think you see that boy.

He'd be old by now. Old as you. But sometimes you see a young man in the middle distance and, for a split second, you convince yourself it's him, and he hasn't aged since that night. You convince yourself your eyes will meet and he'll say he's so sorry he never called. Then he'll take your hand and you'll glide into a parallel last fifty years in which you'll wake up next to him in the present day, and the real last fifty years will all have been a mundane dream that will fizzle from your memory within seconds.

"Are you wearing the jacket right now?" you said.

"I am."

You told me not to talk anymore. To keep the jacket on. To stay on the line with you while you hum a little tune. To sway my hips to your rhythm. To keep swaying. To keep swaying until you were ready to hang up.

I'm still swaying.

I think you've fallen asleep, but I won't hang up.

A Date without Small Talk

I hate small talk, so I thought it was cool when we hugged and you said, "Hi, nice to meet you. Do you think that time existed before the universe was formed?"

We went mini-golfing. I asked you if you thought it was possible that a miniature Earth, maybe the size of one of these golf balls, might exist somewhere inside this normal-sized Earth.

"How do you know we're not already inside this miniature Earth you speak of?" you asked. "How do you know giant clones of us aren't walking around out there, having this same exact conversation?"

"Except I guess they'd be calling it just golf," I said.

The rest of the date might have lasted a minute or a million eons. I don't remember, because you made me feel dizzy, like my world was a vortex on course for a black hole.

Whenever it ended, I asked if I could see you again.

You told me this was inevitable, because the universe is

expanding and will continue to expand until it begins to collapse. Then it will collapse until it has collapsed to nothing. From there, it will start expanding again, and it will expand in exactly the same way it expanded before. All events will be exactly the same. Eventually, it, and we, will arrive back at this exact moment. This has already happened a trillion times before, and it will happen a trillion times again. The universe is trapped in this cycle.

"So yes," you said. "You will see me again. In this iteration of existence or the next."

A day later, I messaged you. I said the weather was nice. I asked how you were doing and what you were getting up to.

I waited for you to message back.

I waited and I waited.

I waited more. I waited longer than it takes for the universe to expand and collapse and then expand again until the moment we first met. I waited for so long that I now have a definitive answer to your question:

No. Time did not exist before the universe got formed. If it did, surely by now I'd have seen you again.

Talk

I'm calling the emergency line but my ear is drowning in dark currents.

Through the flow I almost hear myself telling them I just need someone to talk to and can they please talk to me because I think I'm dying and I don't want to die alone.

They tell me we're not alone.

I'm trying to stop blood leaving my head from behind the lobe but it's like plugging a monsoon with a cork and my hand only pushes the crystals lodged in my skull further into my skull.

They tell me they're sending the aliens and who am I and where am I and where have I been.

I'm listening to myself telling them I need the aliens to get here quick.

They ask me what happened and I tell them there was trouble out here and I went to stop the trouble.

I'm telling them just as I thought I'd stopped the trouble something smashed the back of my head and I didn't see anything but it feels like the whole universe got condensed into a snow globe that collided like a species-shattering meteor into the back of my head and are the aliens coming soon?

They tell me I need to keep talking and they keep asking questions that relate to the real world and I'm not in the real world.

I'm watching those deepening dark currents from my ear flood the ground beneath my head like a black hole and I feel the black hole sucking me into a portal to the future past.

They ask me if I'm still there and tell me to say something just give them a signal because it's really important that I keep talking because I'm getting sucked in.

Once I'm inside time is going to get stretched and warped.

They ask me something else but I don't hear because

I'm sucked in. And time *is* stretched and time *is* warped. I see the future. The future is me waking up in a hospital bed. I'm peeking at my family through bandages. They're telling me I was apparently talking a load of gibberish when I got here, "But what's new?" It hurts when I laugh but I don't mind. The physical wounds heal within weeks. The future

future is more painful. The future future is not being able to go out in public without hearing crunching glass coming behind me instead of innocent footsteps. The future future is dark and rainy nights seeing jaggy shattered vodka bottles covered in blood falling from the sky. The future future is standing in a crowd and looking at the back of someone's head and seeing gashes open up behind their earlobe like black holes that now suck me into the past where

I'm a child. I'm in therapy because I have this compulsion to hit people. They don't do anything special there. They just talk to me. I stop doing it and I grow up and I stop a fight and I get bottled and sucked into a black hole and back into the future future where I'm back in therapy. They ask me if I've considered getting out there. Spending time with other people in the same hole.

He and I talk because there's nothing else to do but talk because it's not like we can go out. He talks gibberish about space even more than I do. Says he's 99% sure he's an alien because that would explain a lot about why the world to him is so fucked up but every cunt else is able to just get on with it. I tell him it got better for me when I started writing down my thoughts. On good days I can get it down to a solid 98.9%.

One time I turn up and he's written something. What he's written is a story about me and what happened to me and of course it's got black holes and aliens in it.

At the end of the story the aliens arrive and pull me out the puddle of black hole and as expected they are green and shrouded in blue light. I don't know who I am or where I am or whether it's the past or the present or the future or future future. What I do hear is myself talking into the phone that's still connected to the emergency line that's lying in the puddle of my blood.

I'm saying thank you

Thank you for just talking to me.

A Whisper from The Sea

I heard about a black hole somewhere in the ocean.

I packed my easel onto a boat and went out there to find it and draw it.

I got too close. The black hole swallowed me up. Turned my canvas into a unit of time. Trapped me in eternity.

You'll never see me again, but do not fret.

I'm always sketching. When you miss me, look out to the horizon. Follow the pencil lines. Your future is all mapped out for you.

The Promise

You asked me to bury you in space, away from gravity.

"Promise?" you said.

"I promise."

When you died, the rest of the family insisted you got put in the ground.

I grew up and became an astronaut. I carry a spade on every mission.

Each time I return, I put a handful of stars on your grave.

I feel the weight lift, bit by bit.

They Cry and Shriek

We can't hear it, but Moons make noises as they circle their planets.

They sing and laugh if their planet is in harmony. They cry and shriek if it is not.

Our Moon has been crying and shrieking for centuries.

We gaze up at the night sky.

"Isn't it beautiful," we say.

Moving The Dust Around

I fell down a trap door in the floor of the universe.

The cellar down here is full of disused stars, old gravity and musty time, all coated in layers of moon dust.

The only thing I can do to alleviate my eternal boredom is to shift that dust, using the vacuum of space.

The Looping

My soul left my body.

With no body, you can't do much except wait.

I watched my children grow up and die. I waited for time to end and loop back to the start. I waited more. I watched my parents get born, grow up, meet.

Then I went back in my body and I started again.

Tides

The Moon is drifting from Earth.

Eventually, we'll lose contact.

We'll gaze at the sky and see it joining the orbit of another planet.

They'll make tides of their own. Not better ones, just different.

Tides that seem right as we watch them lapping those faraway shores.

+0

You've gone solo to another wedding.

It's the section of the day straight after the service, before everyone goes and sits for the speeches and the food. Everyone stands around waiting and drinking sparkling wine and talking. Waiting. Talking. Waiting. Talking and waiting. Everyone, waiting and talking, talking and waiting in couples and in pairs. Everyone, in pairs and couples, talking. Except you. You're alone. Waiting. Drinking. Waiting and drinking.

You're standing. You're hovering. You're taking anxious sips. You're floating between groups of two and groups of four and six. Wherever you float, wherever you hover, you're turning even numbers odd.

$1 + 0 =$ You

You've done the right thing. You've gone and you've locked yourself in a toilet cubicle.

You're locked in the toilet cubicle. You're quaffing

complimentary champagne, flute number five, waiting for it to morph you into some sort of social butterfly or some shit.

You've already used the toilet and flushed the toilet, but you flush the toilet again. The sympathetic groan of the cistern masks the breathing exercises you're now doing — the ones you were taught to do when things get a bit much at work — by the occupational health therapist who later went off for six months with a nervous breakdown.

The cistern's final hisses fade to silence. You flush again. It's the fourth time you've flushed. You contemplate your options. The chatter out there sounded as loud as ever. The talking and the waiting shows no sign of letting up.

You see two ways out.

The cubicle door is Option 1. Back out there to more people talking while you stand and you hover and you wait and you scramble that gentle equilibrium of even numbers.

Option 2? An escape. Down the toilet, Renton from Trainspotting style. Through the sewage pipes, finale of *The Shawshank Redemption* style. You picture it, elation, as you stare back at the venue, now a distance away. You're covered in shit, but you're out. You're alone, but no longer odd.

Did you know that the average person spends six months of their life waiting for a red light to turn green?

The above has nothing to do with anything. I just told you it to pass a speck of time, maybe calm you down a bit.

Hi.

I am your +0 for the rest of the day. I am your future self, from just far enough ahead to tell you this: after two more flushes and a few more deep breaths, right down through your belly, it will be time for you to take Option 1.

That's a nice suit you're wearing. You look far too amazing to get it covered in shit. Plus, you're not that skinny.

I'm here to tell you you'll go out there and, maybe something to do with all those empty champagne flutes you've left around the edges of the room, you'll butt into the first even numbered group you see and… it'll be…

fine.

They'll be glad to have you butt in. Their conversation was drying up before you came. Nobody really likes the talking and waiting bit.

You'll get chatting to a nice lady. She'll be the auntie of the best man who feels like she is, by extension, the auntie of the groom and now therefore, by extension, the auntie of the bride. Something like that. She'll be a town planning consultant. She'll tell you a very interesting fact about how long people wait at traffic lights in a lifetime, then she'll tell you it's actually made up and probably not true, because how could anyone actually know that?

Then the waiting will be over. For the speeches and the food, you'll be sat next to another odd number. You'll ask him where he's been hiding this whole time. He'll tell you he'd found a cloak room. He'll tell you he'd spent at least an hour there, burying his face in people's jackets to smother the sound of his screams of anguish and existential dread. You'll tell him you wish you'd thought of that. You'll tell him you'd spent that whole time looking for a rock hammer.

"To maim all the other guests?" he'll say.

"Something like that," you'll say.

Then you'll agree, the best way forward is to keep drinking.

You'll drink.

You'll dance. With him. With town planner auntie. And the groom's granny. And the bride's uncle Jimmy. And everyone else. You'll belt out the wedding band's versions of 'Livin' on a Prayer' and 'Wonderwall' and you'll invade the stage and encourage everyone else to do the same and even though nobody will, it won't matter, because...

It'll be fine in the end. You'll be sad when it's over.

Anyway.

I'm exhausted now. All that dancing. All that singing. The bruises from the stage dive. I'm going to bed.

I just thought I'd drop in on you before I call a taxi, because I've been where you are now. It was brutal. Really tough. Could have done with somebody like me there in my ear.

So there it is. Have another flush or two. Finish that champagne. Breathe in through the nose and out through the mouth. Get yourself out there. Act amazed when you get told that fake fact about traffic lights and waiting. Dance. Sing. Invade.

And in a few hours, don't forget to check back in on the you of the past.

Snooze

I ran a bath and went for a lie down while I waited.

The smell of lavender made me drift off, and I fell asleep for centuries.

When I woke up, the floodwaters on my floor contained all the sea life in the world.

I waded through fish and whales, seaweed and shipwrecks to turn off the tap.

Then I climbed back onto my floating bed and went back to sleep.

Then We Soar

Whenever I see a comet in the night, I know it's you winking at us.

"Grab on," you whisper through the dark and cloudless sky.

I hold my thumb and forefinger up to one eye and I pinch the tail.

Then we soar between the stars and the universes, shedding gravity and time, sadness and death.

The Grass Is Always Greener in The Stars

"I want to be an Earth child," said the alien who abducted the boy.

So, they swapped lives: UFO for bike.

Nobody told the alien that Earth children grow up, or that he would grow up sad, always staring at the sky, always contemplating former lives and bad decisions, always writing about what's smiling down from the stars.

Silent Grunge Street Disco

Every Saturday evening, I walk to my night shift. As I get to the centre of town, I pass a group of about twenty drunk people. They all have earphones in. They're singing 'Smells Like Teen Spirit' by Nirvana as they mosh out-of-tune down the street, led by a lady wearing a t-shirt that says 'Silent Grunge Street Disco'.

This happens every week.. Same time, same spot, same song, same lady.

Apart from the lady, I never look at the individual faces. They probably change from one Saturday to the next, but I like to think of them as the same; like my life is a repeating groundhog week and I have therefore not aged another seven days since the last time.

When I pass the group, moving in the opposite direction, I don't go round them. I go through them. I imagine their dancing bodies crushing the pent-up angst out of me. In their ears, they hear 'Smells Like Teen Spirit' and feel nirvana. In mine, I hear noise pollution and feel fear.

Surely an inverse scenario is unfolding in some parallel universe –

Every week, they stomp to work through a concrete jungle soundtrack of capitalism. I'm drunk, moshing in the opposite direction with a group of friends, Nirvana in my earlobes. I'm back in the moment I heard that song for the first time. I'm thirteen years old. Their music is what tells me maybe I am wired into this life ok after all.

At work, I stay tuned to this scenario. The clock ticks. The seconds stretch and linger and make me too exhausted to ever get myself out of this rut. I close my eyes. I'm drunk, in a parallel universe. And I'm thirteen years old.

And I will never be a week older than the Saturday before.

What Would Happen If
The Speed of Light Simply Changed

I knew the speed of light had slowed down to a snail's pace when I looked across the street. The people I saw on the other side were from weeks ago.

I knew it when I looked down at what I was eating and saw breakfast, even though I was actually eating dinner.

I knew it when I first laid eyes on my true love, even though our children were already born.

Tonight, I Fall From The Sky

My blood absorbs into my body. My bones heal. The airbag sucks into the steering wheel. The car uncrumples and veers onto the road.

I drive home, backwards.

I unkiss you goodbye and go into the house, where I haunt you until the day we meet.

Acknowledgements

Eternal thanks to the Back Patio Press boys, Cavin Bryce Gonzalez and Zac Smith, for making this with me, for your energy, for the journey. Cavin, thank you for your encouragement, your faith in me, for making me realise this was possible in the first place. Thank you to my two best friends, Richard Jacobs and Stephen McLaren, for being exactly that. Thank you to my parents, for every reason in the universe. Thank you to you, the reader.

Neil Clark is a writer from Edinburgh, Scotland. He didn't discover his love for the written word until his twenties and never thought he'd be writing a bio for his first print collection. But here we are, people. Here we are. He has flash fiction stories published in various online journals, has been nominated for awards such as *Best of the Net* and *Best Small Fictions*, and has placed in some competitions. You can find out more about it at **neilclarkwrites.wordpress.com**.

Twitter: @NeilRClark.

BACK PATIO PRESS CATALOGUE

PHOTOGRAPHS OF MADNESS: INSIDE OUT
by Alec Ivan Fugate

*I COULD BE YOUR NEIGHBOR,
ISN'T THAT HORRIFYING?*
by Cavin Bryce Gonzalez

TIME. WOW.
by Neil Clark

VENICE
by TJ Larkey

NUMBSKULL
by No Glykon

A COMPLETELY NONEXISTENT CARNIVAL
by Cavin Bryce Gonzalez

WATERTOWN
by Daniel Eastman

Visit **https://backpatio.press** for more books and online content. We love you all.
Thank you for reading.

— *Cavin & Zac*

Cover Design

Special thanks to cover designer Brent Woo who has graciously assisted us in creating covers for a number of titles, including *Ghost of Mile 43* by Craig Rodgers (Soft Cartel Press) and *Photographs of Madness: Inside Out* by Alec Ian Fugate (Back Patio Press 2019).

To contact Brent,
you can reach him at: **www.brentwoo.com**

Printed in Great Britain
by Amazon